New Shoes

Jeff MacNelly

CB
CONTEMPORARY
BOOKS
CHICAGO

Library of Congress Cataloging-in-Publication Data

MacNelly, Jeff.
   [Shoe. Selections]
   New shoes / Jeff MacNelly.
      p.   cm.
   Selections from the author's comic strip "Shoe."
   ISBN 0-8092-3627-3
   I. Title.   II. Title: Shoe.
PN6728.S475M3422   1994
741.5'973—dc20   94-21910
                            CIP

Published by Contemporary Books, Inc.
Two Prudential Plaza, Chicago, Illinois 60601-6790
Manufactured in the United States of America
International Standard Book Number: 0-8092-3627-3
10   9   8   7   6   5   4   3   2   1

SKYLER?...CAN YOU TELL ME WHO WAS PRESIDENT BEFORE WOODROW WILSON?

YES.

COULD YOU BE A LITTLE MORE SPECIFIC?

EVERY AMERICAN HAS THE RIGHT TO VOTE FOR WHOEVER OR, INDEED...

WHOMEVER HE OR SHE WANTS,

DEPENDING ON GRAMMATICAL ORIENTATION..

Don't Ask the Perfesser

Dear Perfesser,
    Those double doors in stores and restaurants:

Why is the one I try first always locked?

Don't ask me.

The First Hairball

SO NOW WE'VE GOT A <u>CAT</u> IN THE WHITE HOUSE...

YUP.

PROBABLY HAVE A LITTER BOX IN THE LINCOLN BEDROOM...

THE FIRST PET HAS ALWAYS BEEN A DOG...

EVERYONE KNOWS DOGS ARE SMARTER THAN CATS...

RIGHT.

HECK, THE BUSHES' DOG EVEN WROTE A <u>BOOK</u>!!

MADE A LOT OF MONEY, TOO...

CAN YOU IMAGINE A CAT WRITING A BOOK?...

HAH!

Milliegate: the Aftermath.

RRRING!

ROUND ONE...

CLASS PARTICIPATION IS SUPPOSED TO BE A BIG FACTOR IN MY GRADE IN THIS CLASS...

CLASS?...

YOU HAVE TO APPEAR INVOLVED AND INTERESTED...

TELL ME WHO

BUT WHEN THERE'S A QUESTION...

WAS LINCOLN'S

YOU DON'T WANT TO BE CALLED ON,

AVOID DIRECT EYE CONTACT AT ALL COSTS...

VICE PRESIDENT

DROPPING YOUR PENCIL IS A GREAT TACTIC.

IN 1865?...

TIMING IS EVERYTHING.

YOU WANT TO RAISE YOUR HAND...

BUT AT JUST THE PRECISE MOMENT WHEN THERE'S NO CHANCE SHE'LL CALL ON YOU...

ANYONE?...

...RIGHT ABOUT....

YES, HOWARD?

NOW!

THIS YEAR MY COMPUTER WILL MAKE DOING TAXES A LOT EASIER FOR ME.

AND IT'LL SAVE ME MONEY, TOO.

LAST YEAR I HAD TO RENT A STEP LADDER TO GET TO MY CHECK STUBS...

AS YOU KNOW, I HAVE NEVER TRUSTED ANY POLITICIAN WHO JOGS.

BUT PRESIDENT CLINTON IS DIFFERENT.

HE'S NOT REALLY A JOGGER.

HE'S MORE OF A JIGGLER.

East Virginia Crime Report:

Last Saturday night the Game Warden was summoned to a domestic disturbance at the home of Mr. and Mrs. Wayne R. Ringworm.

Mrs. Ringworm was apparently attempting to take her husband shopping.

Order was quickly restored after the Warden cited Mrs. Ringworm for a violation of the county leash law.

13

14

15

IT'S GOOD TO SEE YOUR CAR IN HERE AGAIN.

Y'KNOW, AFTER YEARS OF MESSING WITH ALL THESE NEW-FANGLED JAPANESE CARS,

IT'S NICE TO WORK ON SOMETHING OLD-FANGLED FOR A CHANGE.

HOW OFTEN DO YOU CHANGE THE OIL IN THIS HEAP?

NEVER.

IT CHANGES ITSELF.

WHAT'S FOR DESSERT?

NO DESSERT TODAY, SORRY.

I MADE A BUNCH OF MY FABULOUS CHEESECAKES LAST NIGHT...

BUT THEY BLEW OUT THE SUSPENSION ON THE DESSERT CART.

Shoe

By Jeff MacNelly

SO, WHAT'S THIS MOVIE RATE?

ONE THUMB FIRMLY DOWN.

– ON THE FLUSH HANDLE.

Movie Review by the Perfesser.

The so-called psycho-thriller, "The Arkansas Cheese Grater Massacres,"

was possibly the worst time I have ever spent in a dark room...

with the possible exception of Melba Fern Hockschwinder's attempted afternoon of unbridled passion in her father's basement workshop in the seventh grade.

The plot is so incredibly stupid,

the violence, gore and bad language so unbelievably gross...

that this reviewer soon found himself on his knees...

gripping the edge of his seat.

ISN'T THAT A MIXED METAPHOR OR SOMETHING?

NOT IF IT'S A TOILET SEAT...

WHAT ARE YOU WORKING ON?

I'M WRITING A NEW, FANCIER MENU.

WHAT'S FRENCH FOR "FRENCH TOAST"?

AREN'T YOU SORT OF PUSHING THE ENVELOPE?

WE IN CONGRESS STAND READY TO HELP THE PRESIDENT.

ADD THAT TO THE LIST...

WHAT LIST IS THAT?

THE ONE THAT STARTS WITH "THE CHECK IS IN THE MAIL."

I TRY TO BE POLITICALLY CORRECT, BUT IT'S HARD.

A VOTE FOR ME IS A VOTE FOR YOU

"POLITICAL" AND "CORRECT"...

THOSE ARE TWO WORDS YOU DON'T OFTEN SEE TOGETHER.

YABBA DABBA... DABBA DOO.

HAVE YOU EVER HAD ANY PROBLEMS WITH THE GUYS IN THE PRESS ROOM?

YEAH, A COUPLE OF TIMES.

BUT YOU KNOW HOW IT IS, YOU'VE GOT TO BE NICE TO THEM...

OR YOUR PANTS COME BACK ALL WRINKLED.

GOT A PROBLEM, FELLA?

YEAH, HOW DO I GET BACK TO CIVILIZATION?

WELL... HEAD NORTH ON THE FREEWAY...

UH HUH...

..'TIL YOU GET LOW ON GAS...

UH HUH...

..THEN COME ON BACK HERE, FILL'ER UP AND I'LL TELL YOU THE REST OF THE WAY...

ALL RIGHT! HERE'S A STORY ABOUT THE ROYAL FAMILY THAT ISN'T A SENSATIONAL PIECE OF GARBAGE!

IT SAYS HERE THAT A HUGE FEMALE EAGLE PICKED UP PRINCE CHARLES BY HIS OVERSIZED EARS AND DIDN'T SET HIM DOWN 'TIL THEY GOT TO SCOTLAND...

AND YOU DON'T CALL THAT SENSATIONAL?

NO. SENSATIONAL WOULD HAVE BEEN IF HE AND THE EAGLE WERE HAVING AN AFFAIR...

HI, I'D LIKE TO HAVE A PIZZA DELIVERED WITH THE FOLLOWING TOPPINGS:

OLIVES, PEPPERONI, A BOX OF PAPER CLIPS,

FOUR BALL-POINT PENS, A STAPLER, SIX POST-IT PADS AND BOX OF COPIER PAPER...

IT SURE SAVES A LOT OF TIME HAVING THE PIZZA PARLOR NEXT DOOR TO THE STATIONERY STORE.

YOU'VE GOT A WIRE CROSSED SOME-WHERE...

HOW CAN YOU TELL?

JUST A HUNCH.

SAY, ISN'T THAT MURPHY BROWN???

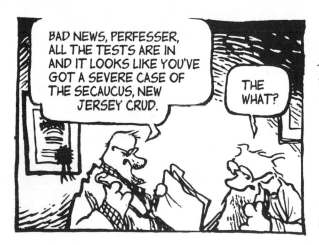

BAD NEWS, PERFESSER, ALL THE TESTS ARE IN AND IT LOOKS LIKE YOU'VE GOT A SEVERE CASE OF THE SECAUCUS, NEW JERSEY CRUD.

THE WHAT?

I'VE NEVER EVEN BEEN TO SECAUCUS...

WELL, YOU'RE GOING NOW, THEY WANT IT BACK...

HI. I'LL BE YOUR WAITRESS THIS EVENING... MY NAME IS ROZ.

IF ANYTHING GOES WRONG...

MY NAME IS FRAN.

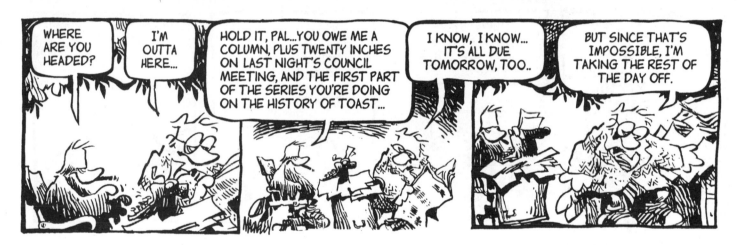

WHERE ARE YOU HEADED?

I'M OUTTA HERE...

HOLD IT, PAL...YOU OWE ME A COLUMN, PLUS TWENTY INCHES ON LAST NIGHT'S COUNCIL MEETING, AND THE FIRST PART OF THE SERIES YOU'RE DOING ON THE HISTORY OF TOAST...

I KNOW, I KNOW... IT'S ALL DUE TOMORROW, TOO..

BUT SINCE THAT'S IMPOSSIBLE, I'M TAKING THE REST OF THE DAY OFF.

HEY, PERFESSER, I NEED YOUR ADVICE ON SOMETHING...

SHOOT.

I'M STARTING A NEW COLUMN ON THE FINE ART OF CIGAR SMOKING, AND I NEED A CATCHY TITLE.

THAT'S EASY...

HOW 'BOUT "THE CIGAR CORNER SEWER."

HOW ARE YOU SPELLING THAT?

Row 1

The Cigar
Corner Sewer
by P.Martin
Shoemaker.

To fully appreciate fine cigars, it's important to recognize the various types of cigar.

There are two basic categories of cigar:

The lit and the unlit.

Row 2

The Cigar
Corner Sewer
by P. Martin
Shoemaker.

Guys, don't be afraid to fire up a nice cigar in a crowd.

That first big puff sends out a distinctive signal loud and clear to members of the opposite sex:

"Leave the room."

Row 3

The Cigar
Corner Sewer
by P. Martin
Shoemaker.

Don't be shy about being a cigar smoker.

Lighting up a cigar in polite company is a great way to start a conversation.

It's an even better way to end one.

By Jeff MacNelly

IS IT HAPPY HOUR YET?

I THINK IT JUST ENDED...

ONE FOR LUNCH, PLEASE...
RIGHT THIS WAY...

AND WHAT KIND OF IMPORTED BEER DO YOU HAVE?
WE HAVE SEVERAL:

THERE'S BECHT'S, Recht's, LOO CAO, Old Yeller,

ShingFa,... El Loboloco
Wild Rhino, CRY of the LOON.

Harrigan's, O'Noodle's AND FARBISSENER LITE

WELL, WHAT'LL IT BE?

A DRAFT.

I'D RATHER LISTEN TO THEM THAN PAY FOR THEM...

27

By Jeff MacNelly

HOWDY, PARDNER!

DOODY, PARDNER...

SAY, WHO WAS THAT STRANGER IN THE FANCY GET-UP?

DON'T KNOW.

HE DIDN'T LEAVE A NAME...

BUT HE TOOK ALL MY TAX RETURNS FROM THE PAST SIX YEARS,...

WASTED THREE MONTHS OF MY TIME,...

AND TURNED ME DOWN FOR A NEW MORTGAGE.

BUT HE LEFT THIS COMPLIMENTARY, SOLAR-POWERED MINI-CALCULATOR WITH THIS SILVER BANK LOGO ON IT...

WHY, THAT'S NO STRANGER, PARDNER..

IT'S THE LOAN RANGER!

HIYO, SILVERADO, AWAY!!

The Cigar Corner Sewer by P. Martin Shoemaker

Dear Mr. Shoemaker:
    I'd like to enjoy smoking cigars on a regular basis...

but I find that they burn my tongue. What can I do?

Next time try putting the other end in your mouth.

Dear Editor:
    Give the President a break! He's only been in office a few weeks! Give him a little time before you dump all over him, okay?

..as we were saying,

DON'T BE SO HARD ON YOURSELF, COSMO. A LOT OF PEOPLE ARE COMPUTER ILLITERATE.

THAT'S NOT EXACTLY MY PROBLEM...

I'M COMPUTER MANUAL ILLITERATE.

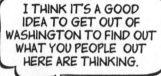

WHAT THE HECK BRINGS YOU OUT HERE TO ROZ'S, SENATOR?

JUST A LITTLE VISIT TO THE HOME STATE, BOYS, ... TO MINGLE WITH MY CONSTITUENTS.

I THINK IT'S A GOOD IDEA TO GET OUT OF WASHINGTON TO FIND OUT WHAT YOU PEOPLE OUT HERE ARE THINKING.

ACTUALLY, WE WERE JUST THINKING HOW NICE IT WAS THAT YOU WERE THERE AND WE WERE HERE.

I'VE BEEN THINKING, WIZ ... WHAT IF THIS THING IS JUST ANOTHER CB RADIO-- ANOTHER EIGHT-TRACK?

SAY WHAT?...

I MEAN, WHAT IF THE COMPUTER IS JUST ANOTHER FAD?

BITE YOUR TONGUE.

MY POLLS ARE STILL WAY DOWN... I DON'T GET IT... IF THEY DON'T LIKE ME, WHY DO THEY KEEP SENDING ME TO WASHINGTON?

GEE, THAT'S HARD TO SAY...

MAYBE THEY JUST WANT YOU OUT OF TOWN.

WHAT DID THE DOCTOR SAY?

HE SAID THAT ONE LEG WAS SHORTER THAN THE OTHER.

BUT WHEN I ASKED FOR A SECOND OPINION,

HE TOLD ME THAT ONE LEG WAS LONGER THAN THE OTHER.

I'D LIKE TO TRADE SOME OF MY FREQUENT FLYER MILES.

CERTAINLY, SIR.

YOU ARE ENTITLED TO ONE ROUNDTRIP COACH...

I'D SETTLE FOR ONE-WAY LEGROOM.

HOW DO YOU MANAGE TO FLY WITH A BODY LIKE THAT?

I HAVE TO FLY LIKE THIS...

MY COMPANY MAKES ME FLY COACH.

SORRY, PERFESSER, BUT IT'S OUT OF MY HANDS NOW... IT'S ALL UP TO THE MAN UPSTAIRS.

MY REPAIR IS NOW IN THE HANDS OF GOD?

CLOSE... BIG BOB THE ANTIQUE PARTS MANAGER...

VERTICAL STORAGE SYSTEMS ARE SO INACCESSIBLE ...

IT'S TIME TO TEST A HORIZONTAL SYSTEM...

I'M TIRED OF OUR PAPER CONSTANTLY PICKING ON THE PRESIDENT...

YOU'RE RIGHT, IT HAS BEEN PRETTY NONSTOP. MAYBE WE SHOULD SHIFT OUR EMPHASIS...

AND PICK ON THE VICE PRESIDENT FOR A WHILE...

HOW DO YOU FEEL ABOUT THE PRESIDENT'S ENERGY TAX PROPOSAL?

HE CAN TAX ENERGY ALL HE WANTS... HE HAS MY TOTAL AND COMPLETE SUPPORT...

THAT'S PRETTY DARN GENEROUS OF YOU...

NOT REALLY, I HAVEN'T HAD ANY ENERGY SINCE THE CARTER ADMINISTRATION.

IS THIS YOUR HOUSE WINE?

NOT EXACTLY. THIS IS MUCH CHEAPER, BUT IT TRAVELS WELL...

YOU DON'T MEAN...

YES. OUR MOBILE HOME WINE.

I'D LIKE TO RENT A CAR THAT MAKES A REAL STATEMENT.

SOMETHING MY TRUE ADMIRERS WOULD EXPECT TO SEE ME IN... SOMETHING THAT REFLECTS MY PERSONALITY...

HAVE YOU TRIED MEL'S RENT-A-WRECK BEHIND THE AIR FREIGHT TERMINAL?

I HAVE A SHORT STATEMENT TO MAKE.

AFTER WHICH I WILL ATTEMPT TO FLEE TO THE AIRPORT.

WE ARE FACING TOUGH TIMES...

WE HAVE TO CUT BACK...

WE'LL HAVE TO SPEND LESS.

WE MUST EXPECT TO PAY MORE TAXES.

IN SHORT, WE HAVE TO MAKE SACRIFICES!

WHAT DO YOU MEAN "WE"? THAT'S THE ROYAL WE.

—A FIGURE OF SPEECH... MEANING YOU.

43

WHAT'S THAT AWFUL SMELL?

THE SALAD.

HEY, THIS ISN'T FETA CHEESE.

RIGHT.

I SAID FETID CHEESE.

WHAT'S THAT YOU'RE READING?

"WOMEN BEHIND BARS."

DON'T GET EXCITED.

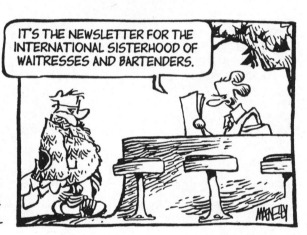

IT'S THE NEWSLETTER FOR THE INTERNATIONAL SISTERHOOD OF WAITRESSES AND BARTENDERS.

POSTCARD?

YEAH... FROM AN EX-BOYFRIEND.

OH WELL, I GUESS HIS HEART'S IN THE RIGHT PLACE...

SASKATCHEWAN.

OF COURSE I WON'T USE YOUR NAME... THANKS FOR THE TIP!

GEE... BEING A REPORTER IS A LOT LIKE BEING A PLUMBER...

YOU SIT BY THE PHONE AND WAIT FOR THE LEAKS.

YOU PEOPLE HAVE LOST A PACKAGE OF MINE... I WANT YOU TO TRACE IT IMMEDIATELY!

SORRY, SIR, WE DON'T TRACE PACKAGES...

HOWEVER, IF YOU LIKE, OUR STAFF ARTIST WILL BE GLAD TO DO AN ABSTRACT SKETCH.

WELL, I'VE FINALLY FINISHED THAT STORY ABOUT GORE-TEX I'VE BEEN WORKING ON.

YOU DID A STORY ABOUT WATERPROOF CLOTHING?

NO, I DID A STORY ABOUT THE VICE PRESIDENT AND HIS NEW TEN-GALLON HAT.

IF YOU SPENT AS MUCH TIME ON YOUR HOMEWORK AS YOU DO DREAMING UP EXCUSES FOR NOT DOING IT...

YOU'D BE A STRAIGHT 'A' STUDENT.

I KNOW, BUT THEN, I'D SO MISS THESE LITTLE CHATS ...

THAT'LL BE EIGHT BUCKS.

FOR A PIECE OF "CHOCOLATE DECADENCE FUDGE PIE"?

THE SIN TAX JUST KICKED IN.

WHATEVER YOU DO, DON'T ORDER THE SUBMARINE SANDWICH, SHE MAKES THEM AHEAD OF TIME.

SO, WHAT'S WRONG WITH THAT?

SHE STORES THEM IN THE LOBSTER TANK.

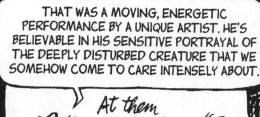
THAT WAS A MOVING, ENERGETIC PERFORMANCE BY A UNIQUE ARTIST. HE'S BELIEVABLE IN HIS SENSITIVE PORTRAYAL OF THE DEEPLY DISTURBED CREATURE THAT WE SOMEHOW COME TO CARE INTENSELY ABOUT.

At them FLICKS...

IT'S CLEAR HE IS THE MASTER OF THE GENRE.

ALSO, I LOVE IT WHEN HE GOES "WOO WOO."

I AGREE! DAFFY DUCK HAS NEVER BEEN BETTER.

At them 'icks...

NOT ANOTHER SPIN-OFF.

HONEST, THIS IS THE BEST ONE YET...

I'VE BEEN WAITING FOR THIS FOR MONTHS.

"STAR TREK BABIES: THE GENERATION AFTER THE GENERATION AFTER THAT."

I BUY A TALKING SCALE AND THE FIRST TIME I USE THE DARN THING IT BREAKS DOWN.

WHEN I WAS A BOY, THINGS WERE MADE TO LAST.

THEY SURE DON'T MAKE JUNK LIKE THEY USED TO.

OH WAIT A SECOND, I'M STANDING ON ITS TONGUE...

YOU KNOW, THOSE EXERCISE CONTRAPTIONS ACTUALLY WORK IF YOU USE THEM CORRECTLY.

OH, COME ON!...

NO KIDDING. NEXT TIME YOU FEEL _REALLY_ HUNGRY...

STICK A THIGHMASTER IN YOUR MOUTH.

MEXICAN NIGHT AGAIN?

YES. I FIND MEXICAN FOOD VERY VERSATILE.

ME, TOO.

I'VE USED YOUR GUACAMOLE TO FIX CRACKS IN MY DRYWALL.

@#☆!!

DON'T MIND HIM, ROZ, HIS HEART'S IN THE RIGHT PLACE.

I'M SURE IT IS.

☆#@!!

BUT HIS MOUTH ISN'T.

IT'S 78 DEGREES AND BREEZY...

..BUT WITH GUSTS UP TO 20 MPH.

SO THE WINDCHILL FACTOR WILL MAKE IT FEEL LIKE 74 OUT THERE...

YOU KNOW... THERE ARE TWO KINDS OF PEOPLE IN THE WORLD.

I KNOW... I KNOW...

THOSE WHO DIVIDE THE WORLD INTO TWO KINDS OF PEOPLE...

..AND THOSE WHO DON'T.

I FIGURED OUT A WAY TO GET MORE EXERCISE AND EAT WHATEVER I WANT.

I MOVED THE REFRIGERATOR.

THERE IS AN ITCH SO PRIVATE, SO PERSONAL...

..THAT WE'RE GOING TO DISCUSS IT RIGHT HERE IN THIS COMMERCIAL

DURING YOUR DINNER.

DID YOU FINISH THAT EDITORIAL ABOUT MRS. CLINTON?

THE ONE ABOUT THE DANGERS OF HAVING AN UNELECTED FEMALE AUTHORITY FIGURE MEDDLING IN OUR LIVES?

I DECIDED AGAINST IT.

MOM THREATENED TO CANCEL HER SUBSCRIPTION.

THESE SESSIONS ARE HELPING.

GOOD.

I'M FEELING A LOT BETTER ABOUT MYSELF.

GOOD.

I'VE FINALLY GOTTEN IN TOUCH WITH MY FEELINGS.

THAT'S NICE.

NOW LET'S SEE IF YOU CAN GET IN TOUCH WITH YOUR STRIKE ZONE.

Define the
following:

Swimsuit

When one fish takes
another fish to court.

♪♫

I LOVE TO
SING OUT LOUD
WHEN I'M
ALONE IN MY
CAR.

I GUESS THAT
MAKES ME A CLOSET
EXTROVERT.

Y'KNOW,
DOC, I CAN
CURE YOUR
HICCUPS...

HIC...
REALLY?

SURE, BUT YOU MAY
EXPERIENCE SOME
DISCOMFORT.

OKAY
HIC

HILLARY RODHAM
CLINTON WANTS TO
LOOK OVER YOUR
BOOKS!

ULP!

CRUEL, BUT
REMARKABLY
EFFECTIVE...

A Looner Eclipse

HELLO, SUSAN?...

I'M SORRY! SUZANNE! OF COURSE!!

YEAH, WELL,... THIS IS LOON.

WE MET AT THE PARTY...

NO... SATURDAY NIGHT...

HUH?

NO, THAT WAS WOODY.

I'M A LOT TALLER THAN HIM.

I'M THE GUY WITH THE GOGGLES AND THE ROLLER SKATES.

HELLO?...

THESE MATING CALLS ARE ALWAYS HELL.

63

I TRY TO TALK TO MY NEPHEW, BUT I CAN'T SEEM TO GET THROUGH TO HIM.

WELL, YOU'RE MAKING ONE OF THE MOST COMMON MISTAKES IN THE ENGLISH LANGUAGE.

WHAT'S THAT?

USING IT TO COMMUNICATE WITH A KID.

THERE IS SO MUCH AWESOME POTENTIAL IN MY MACHINERY.

I HAVE SO MUCH INTELLIGENCE, SO MUCH POWER, SO MUCH MEMORY.

IT'S TOO BAD I HAVE SUCH LIMITED TOOLS TO WORK WITH...

HEY, YOU'RE STARTING TO OOZE THERE...

THANKS, I KNOW...

I'M LATE MIGRATING NORTH THIS YEAR...

MUST BE TOUGH BEING A CHOCOLATE MOOSE.

I FINISHED.

THIS IS AWFULLY LATE...

THAT'S OKAY.

JUST CHANGE IT TO "CLINTON'S FIRST 131 DAYS".

Film Critic's Corner

This film was well over three hours long.

It forced me to think about the pain involved in trying to end a long relationship.

In this case, the relationship between me and my seat.

YOU'VE WRITTEN A COLUMN ABOUT A PLACE THAT 80 PERCENT OF OUR READERS CAN'T FIND ON A MAP.

SO?

IT'S ON THE EDITORIAL PAGE.

80 PERCENT OF OUR READERS CAN'T FIND THAT EITHER.

 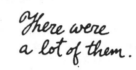 

68

Vocabulary Quiz:

Liposuction

?

The best way to eat soup.

I SUPPORT THE "MOTOR-VOTER" BILL, BUT IT DOESN'T GO FAR ENOUGH.

TO BE FAIR, I'VE INTRODUCED THE "BOATER-VOTER" BILL...

TO REGISTER REPUBLICANS IN YACHT CLUBS.

YUKKO...

UH, ROZ?... CLEAR COLAS, CLEAR DETERGENT... THAT'S ALL FINE.

BUT I DRAW THE LINE AT CLEAR KETCHUP.

WITH OUR NEW SYSTEM WE'VE BEEN ABLE TO REDUCE OUR PAPERWORK BY 60 PERCENT.

TROUBLE IS...

NOW IT'S SO SMALL WE CAN'T READ THE TYPE.

IN RESPONSE TO HANDGUN VIOLENCE, I SUPPORTED THE BRADY BILL...

AND NOW, TO HELP COMBAT TV VIOLENCE...

I HAVE INTRODUCED THE BRADY BUNCH BILL,

WHICH MANDATES A SEVEN-DAY WAITING PERIOD BEFORE TURNING ON A TELEVISION.

Dear Editor,
In this world that is becoming more and more fragmented,

how can we at last achieve real harmony

among all the diverse interest groups?

Have the groups hire themselves some Pips.

OLD?! YOU'RE NOT OLD!!

BITE YOUR TONGUE!

- BUT NOT WITH YOUR OLD ADHESIVE.

IF THE COMPUTER IS TURNING THE WORLD INTO A GLOBAL VILLAGE,

AND I CAN'T FIGURE OUT HOW TO USE THE THING...

DOES THAT MAKE ME A GLOBAL VILLAGE IDIOT?

UH, ROZ... THIS IS A LOT OF PANCAKES...

OH, SORRY.

BLAT!

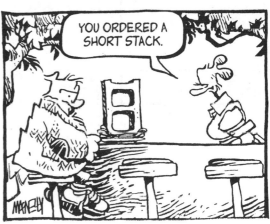

YOU ORDERED A SHORT STACK.

YES, THE PRESIDENT IS IN TROUBLE. HE'S ENGAGED IN A STRUGGLE WHICH WILL DEFINE HIS PRESIDENCY.

"DEFINE" HIS PRESIDENCY? WHAT'S THAT MEAN IN ACTUAL ENGLISH?

WELL, WHEN THE PRESIDENT ASKS HOW HE'S DOING...

FEWER PEOPLE ARE SAYING "FINE."

Dear Editor,

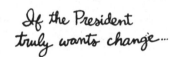

If the President truly wants change....

I believe he first needs to take a closer look at home...

— like under the sofa cushions.

DO YOU HAVE ANY COMMENT ABOUT THE LATEST POLL?

I DON'T TRUST POLLS.

THIS ONE SAYS POLITICIANS RATE VERY LOW ON A LIST OF WHO PEOPLE SAY THEY TRUST.

AND WHO ARE WE AHEAD OF ON THIS LIST?

UH... POLLSTERS.

I REST MY CASE.

84

YOU KNOW, BOB HERE HAS GOTTEN ALONG VERY WELL ALL HIS LIFE WITH ONLY A ONE-WORD VOCABULARY.

PIZZA!

KEEP IN MIND IT'S NOT ONLY WHAT YOU SAY BUT HOW YOU SAY IT...

I'LL HAVE THE PRESIDENTIAL BREAKFAST.

WHAT'S THAT?

YOU ORDER CORN FLAKES, YOU GET YOGURT AND GRANOLA...

..BUT YOU GET TO PAY FOR STEAK AND EGGS.

SO... WAS ELVIS SIGHTED AGAIN IN MADONNA'S SOCK DRAWER?

NO. THIS WEEK A CANNIBAL GOT SICK AFTER EATING HARRISON FORD.

UFO
BIGFOOT MARRIES KENNEDY

AHA! INDYGESTION...

WHAP

86

HOW DID YOU DO ON YOUR MAKE-UP TEST?

PRETTY POORLY, I'M AFRAID...

LET'S FACE IT, I DON'T KNOW THE FIRST THING ABOUT MASCARA.

SAY, ISN'T THAT GUY STEALING SECOND BASE?

WHY YES, I BELIEVE HE IS...

WELL, AREN'T YOU GOING TO DO SOMETHING ABOUT IT?

HECK NO.

WHAT IF HE'S ARMED?

OH, I'M SORRY. I DIDN'T SEE YOU THERE. HAVE YOU BEEN WAITING LONG?

NO, I HAVEN'T BEEN WAITING LONG, NOT LONG AT ALL...

..IN GEOLOGIC TERMS.

SHOE

By Jeff MacNelly

ARE YOU WITH THE CONCERNED SCIENTISTS?

WHO CARES?

IN RESPONSE TO MASSIVE BUDGET CUTS FOR RESEARCH AND DEVELOPMENT...

WE, THE CONCERNED SCIENTISTS OF PLANET EARTH, HAVE CALLED THIS JOINT PRESS CONFERENCE TO EXPRESS OUR OUTRAGE TO THE SENATOR.

AS YOU CAN SEE, WE HAVE FITTED THIS SPECIAL DEVICE OVER THE SENATOR'S HEAD.

HE WILL NOW BE ABLE TO VISUALIZE AN ENTIRELY NEW WORLD...

AND WITH THE SPECIAL GLOVES HE'LL BE ABLE ACTUALLY TO MANIPULATE HIS NEW ENVIRONMENT...

IN EFFECT, WE HOPE THE SENATOR WILL BE ABLE TO SEE THE FUTURE...

WHAT DO YOU CALL THIS?

VIRTUAL REALITY.

WOW!...THE COLORS!!

 Caution:

The Sturgeon General has determined that the following pun could be hazardous to your intelligence.

 GROSS!... HERE'S A TV MOVIE ABOUT A KILLER WHO STALKS STREET ENTERTAINERS...

DON'T TELL ME...

 THEY'RE CALLING IT "A MIME IS A TERRIBLE THING TO WASTE."

 WAK

 I HAVE A GENERAL RULE OF THUMB IN LIFE:

 FORGET ABOUT THE FAT LADY SINGING...

 IT AIN'T OVER 'TIL THE CHECK CLEARS.

 IS THAT FOUR ON THE FLOOR?

NO, FIVE.

 I DRANK ONE ON THE WAY OVER.

Shoe
By Jeff MacNelly

THESE BUDGET CUTS LOOK PAINFUL...

SURE.

PAPER CUTS ALWAYS ARE.

TO GET THIS DEFICIT UNDER CONTROL, WE NEED MORE SPENDING CUTS!

BUT DOESN'T THAT MEAN CUTTING ENTITLEMENTS?

NO SIR!

THIS SENATOR IS NOT VOTING FOR ENTITLEMENT CUTS!!

NOT THIS TIME...

I LEARNED MY LESSON A FEW YEARS BACK...

I'M STILL SMARTING FROM THESE ENTITLEMENT STAB WOUNDS.

THERE'S A MENTAL HEALTH ADVISORY OUT TODAY... THE TEMPER-HUMIDITY INDEX IS EXPECTED TO REACH RECORD LEVELS...

HUH?

THAT MEANS HE'LL GET REAL MAD TODAY, AS USUAL, BUT BECAUSE OF THE HUMIDITY,...

IT'LL FEEL A WHOLE LOT WORSE.

IN THE POLITICS OF THIS STATE, I'M PROUD TO SAY I'M A PROMINENT FIGURE.

Belfry for RESIDENT

RIGHT.

A BIG ZERO.

Belfry for RESIDENT

HOW 'BOUT A NICE "FACE-DOWN SUNSET SIESTA"?...

WHAT'S IN IT?

THREE KINDS OF RUM, A CELERY STALK, CHUNKS OF PINEAPPLE AND A WHOLE GRAIN PRETZEL.

GREAT! HIGH-FIBER BOOZE.

Shoe By Jeff MacNelly

THIS IS **AWFUL**!

MOM?... TELL ME TO TURN OFF THE TV, OKAY?...

ANOTHER NEW CABLE CHANNEL? WHAT'S ON?

LET'S SEE... AT 7 PM, IT'S "WHY DON'T YOU GO OUTSIDE AND PLAY?"

7:30 — "NO, YOU CAN'T EAT IN FRONT OF THE TV."

AT 8PM THERE'S "DON'T SIT SO CLOSE!"... 8:30 IS "BUT YOU'VE SEEN THIS BEFORE."

AT 9 WE HAVE "YOU'RE RUINING YOUR EYESIGHT." 9:30 — "DON'T YOU HAVE SOMETHING TO READ?"

10 O'CLOCK: "ARE YOU SURE YOU'VE DONE **ALL** YOUR HOMEWORK?"

10:30 — "TURN THAT DOWN."

AND AT 11 PM, "GO TO BED!"

WHAT A SECOND... WHAT STATION **IS** THIS?

PDN.

THE PARENTAL DISCRETION NETWORK.

I'D LIKE TO REORGANIZE MY DEBT STRUCTURE.

OKAY...

LOOKING AT THE RED INK ON YOUR BALANCE SHEET HERE...

I'D SAY YOUR ENTIRE STRUCTURE IS ELIGIBLE FOR FEDERAL FLOOD RELIEF.

LOANS

THIS GUY IS SUCH AN INSECT!... I DON'T SEE HOW ANYONE COULD VOTE FOR HIM...

WELL, I DID...

HOW COULD YOU?

WELL, I SAW HIM AS THE LESSER OF TWO WEEVILS.

HEY, I HEAR THIS IS ONE OF THOSE POWER LUNCH PLACES.

YOU'RE RIGHT, BUT ONLY ON TUESDAYS.

THAT'S WHEN ROZ DOES HER FAMOUS VEAL SCALLOPINI.

YOU NEED POWER TOOLS TO CUT IT.

WHAT'S THE SOUP DU JOUR?

MANHATTAN CLAM CHOWDER.

NO THANKS...

I ONLY EAT CLAMS THAT ARE RAISED IN THE COUNTRY.

WE NEED TO DO SOMETHING TO GET SOME FAST MEDIA ATTENTION...

THAT'S EASY.

GO TO THE PRESS ROOM...

AND BREAK THE COFFEE MACHINE.

HOW DID MY PLEA BARGAIN GO?

WELL, THANKS TO YOUR HIRING ME AS YOUR ATTORNEY...

AND THE FACT THAT YOU DRIVE THE UGLIEST CAR IN THE COUNTY...

I MANAGED TO GET YOUR PARKING TICKET REDUCED TO SECOND DEGREE LITTERING.

SHoe
By Jeff MacNelly

JUST A FEW BUGS IN YOUR IGNITION SYSTEM...

AND A BIRD'S NEST IN YOUR AIR FILTER.

THE TIMING WAS OFF AND YOU NEEDED NEW POINTS AND PLUGS.

BUT THAT'S EXPECTED IN A CAR THIS OLD.

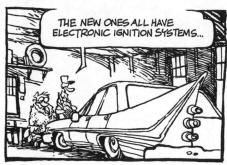

THE NEW ONES ALL HAVE ELECTRONIC IGNITION SYSTEMS...

— SMALL COMPUTERS THAT CONTROL FUEL FLOW AND IGNITION.

SO A TUNE-UP IS MUCH EASIER FOR US NOWADAYS.

BUT ISN'T THAT A HIGH-TECH JOB NOW?... NAH.

IT'S A HIGH PRIEST JOB.

COMPUTER REPAIR

OH NO!

THE DREADED "WHAT I DID LAST SUMMER" ESSAY!

I HATE THIS.

I HAVE TO FIND 400 WORDS FOR "NOTHING."

GO BACK TO YOUR DESK AND THINK OF SOMETHING TO WRITE ABOUT!

NO, WE DON'T NEED AN EDITORIAL ABOUT LIGHT BULBS.

The new round of peace talks has been postponed

to give the parties a chance...

to clear the rubble from the last round of peace talks.

HOW ARE YOU AND THE PRESIDENT GETTING ALONG THESE DAYS?

WELL, WE HAVE OUR DIFFERENCES, OF COURSE... BUT WE'RE STILL ON SPEAKING TERMS.

IN FACT, HE CALLED ME AFTER MY AMENDMENT WAS VOTED DOWN.

WHAT DID HE SAY?

"NANNY NANNY BOO BOO" WAS I BELIEVE THE GIST OF IT.

WELL, AFTER MONTHS OF EDITORIALS ATTACKING THE HIGHWAY DEPARTMENT, THEY'VE GIVEN UP ON THE 50 MILLION-DOLLAR BYPASS AROUND TOWN.

GREAT NEWS!

NOT REALLY. NOW THEY SAY THEY'LL ACCOMPLISH THE SAME THING WITH 50 BUCKS' WORTH OF NEW SIGNS.

THEY'RE MAKING THE SPEED LIMIT 65 DOWN MAIN STREET.

I HAVE TO DRIVE INTO THE CITY TONIGHT...

I HATE THAT. I'M ALWAYS AFRAID MY CAR WILL GET STOLEN.

NOT ME. I'VE GOT THE ULTIMATE HEAVY-DUTY ANTI-THEFT SYSTEM.

REALLY? WHAT IS IT?

A RUSTED-OUT '59 DESOTO.

WHY DO WE HAVE TO LEARN THIS STUFF ANYHOW?

IT'S GOOD FOR YOUR MENTAL DISCIPLINE, SKYLER.

AND IT'LL HELP YOU IN LATER LIFE...

RIGHT.

IN CASE I LAND A JOB IN A VERB CONJUGATION PLANT.

INTERACTIVE TELEVISION?

IT WILL SOON REVOLUTIONIZE THE WAY WE USE TV.

DO YOU REALIZE WHAT WE'LL GET WHEN WE'RE ABLE TO MANIPULATE THE FORMATION AND IMAGES ON THE SCREEN?

YEAH, A BIGGER AND LOUDER VERSION OF "GAME BOY".

THIS DESK HAS 47 SEPARATE COMPARTMENTS THAT ORGANIZE THE FLOW OF MY PAPERWORK.

THEY'RE LIKE TRIBUTARIES THAT CARRY MEMOS AND PAPERS RELENTLESSLY DOWNSTREAM...

SO, MY DESK IS NOT JUST A MESS...

IT'S A FORCE OF NATURE.

THIS NEW POCKET COMPUTER WILL REORGANIZE YOUR OFFICE!!

NO, IT WON'T.

SURE IT WILL! IT CAN STORE EVERYTHING YOU HAVE IN THAT FILE DRAWER.

NO, IT CAN'T.

LOOK, WHAT ARE YOU CURRENTLY FILING IN THERE?

LET'S SEE...

... AND TWO BROKEN ANSWERING MACHINES, ONE GALOSH, AND A BOX OF THE WRONG SIZE COFFEE FILTERS.

I SAID ELEVEN ◎★♯!! HAPPY MEALS.

THANK YOU

BOILED SKINLESS CHICKEN BREAST...

DRY WHOLE WHEAT TOAST...

A HALF GRAPEFRUIT AND TWO LARGE GLASSES OF WATER.

WHY DOES THE HEART HEALTHY DIET HAVE TO BE SO DISHEARTENING?

 OH NO... IS THIS GUY GONNA HIT ON ME?...

 OH NO... IS THIS GUY GONNA HIT ON HER?

 EXCUSE ME... I'M COSMO FISHHAWK... YES?

 I COULDN'T HELP NOTICING THAT YOU'RE HERE ALONE...

 I WONDER IF YOU'D CARE TO JOIN ME FOR DINNER. OH, THANKS VERY MUCH,

 BUT I'M JUST COMING OUT OF A TRAUMATIC RELATIONSHIP...

 SO I'M REALLY NOT READY TO START DATING AGAIN RIGHT NOW...

 HEY, I UNDERSTAND...

 LIFE'S TOO SHORT... YES.

 AND, FRANKLY, SO ARE YOU.

By Jeff MacNelly

AH, MONDAY!

~ A QUIET RESPITE FROM THE HECTIC FRENZY OF THE WEEKEND.

I SECRETLY LOVE MONDAY MORNINGS...

I LIKE TO GET TO THE OFFICE REAL EARLY...

BEFORE ANYONE ELSE SHOWS UP, AND BEFORE THE PHONE STARTS RINGING...

I CAN HAVE A QUIET CUP OF COFFEE...

RELAX AND PUT MY FEET UP...

AND MAKE A LIST OF THE THINGS I NEED TO DO TO GET THE WEEK OFF TO A GOOD START.

WHOMP!

1. Fix chair.

YOU THINK YOU CAN REALLY PAY FOR THIS HEALTH CARE REFORM WITH A CIGARETTE TAX?

CERTAINLY.

WE'VE GOT IT ALL FIGURED OUT.

IT COMES TO ABOUT $4700 A PACK.

YOU STILL THINK YOU'LL BE ABLE TO CUT THE DEFICIT?

OF COURSE! WE'VE RUN THE NUMBERS ON THAT...

WHAT ABOUT THESE NEW ESTIMATES ABOUT THE ECONOMY?

WE'VE RUN THOSE NUMBERS CLEAR OUT OF TOWN.

WE'LL NEVER BALANCE THE BUDGET. IT SIMPLY DOESN'T ADD UP...

IT'S TIME WE GOT AT THE ROOT OF THIS PROBLEM ONCE AND FOR ALL.

THEREFORE, I'M CALLING ON THE PRESIDENT TO FORM A TASK FORCE...

TO REFORM ARITHMETIC.

WELL, IF ALL I READ IS TRUE...

I'M REALLY LOOKING FORWARD TO THE COMING INFORMATION EXPLOSION.

I JUST HOPE IT'S POWERFUL ENOUGH...

TO BREAK UP MY INFORMATION LOGJAM.

SO THAT'S WHAT FIBER OPTICS IS?

YUP, THAT'S IT IN A NUTSHELL.

THAT'S A RELIEF.

I THOUGHT IT WAS ANOTHER NEW CEREAL.

The Cigar Cornersewer

by P. Martin Shoemaker

Recently I test-smoked the new Che Guevara "Revolutione."

Not only did it look disgusting, it burnt my tongue, stank up the room, and offended everyone within noseshot.

In short, it was everything you look for in a fine cigar.

 NEW MENU?

 GEE, DO YOU THINK AMERICA IS READY FOR SCRATCH-AND-SNIFF MENUS?

 WHAT'LL IT BE, SHOE?

 I THINK I'D LIKE SOMETHING SIMPLE...

 SOMETHING WITH NO FAT.

 SOMETHING WITH NO CHOLESTEROL.

 AND ZERO CALORIES.

 -YET TOTALLY SATISFYING.

 -SOMETHING I CAN GET MY TEETH INTO.

 OH NO...

 YES!

 THE CIGAR: AMERICA'S PERFECT SNACK FOOD.

WHEN I START IT UP IN THE MORNING IT MAKES A LOUD CLANGING SOUND.

WELL, LEAVE IT HERE AND COME BACK AFTER LUNCH.

WE'LL TRY STARTING IT IN THE AFTERNOON.

I FOUND OUT WHAT WAS CLOGGING UP YOUR FUEL LINE...

GREAT!

NOT REALLY.

IT'S YOUR CARBURETOR.

SENATOR, WILL YOU BE SEEKING ANOTHER TERM IN OFFICE?

YES, I WILL.

BUT IN THESE CYNICAL TIMES WHEN THE WORD "POLITICIAN" HAS SUCH NEGATIVE CONNOTATIONS...

FIRST I'LL HAVE TO SEEK A NEW TERM FOR "POLITICIAN".

In the Administration's continuing effort to streamline government,

the Small Business Administration has been downsized.

It's now called the Weeny Business Administration.

I DON'T KNOW WHY THIS PLACE IS ALWAYS SUCH A MESS.

THEY SAY IT PROBABLY HAS SOMETHING TO DO WITH EARLY CHILDHOOD TOILET TRAINING.

THAT MAKES SENSE.

I ALWAYS WAS AFRAID OF RUNNING LOW ON PAPER.

HEY, THESE CIGARS AREN'T AS BAD FOR YOU AS CIGARETTES...

IN THE LONG RUN THOSE CIGARS WILL MAKE YOU SHORT OF BREATH.

BIG DEAL.

IN THE REAL LONG RUN WE'LL ALL BE SHORT OF BREATH.

TO DRAMATIZE OUR EFFORTS TO REINVENT GOVERNMENT, I'VE HAULED OUT THESE PILES OF FEDERAL PAPERWORK.

SO WHAT'S THE FORKLIFT FOR?

THAT'S OUR FIRST REINVENTION.

IT'S THE NEW, IMPROVED FEDERAL PAPERWEIGHT.

WHAT'S THE PROBLEM?

IT'S THIS OLD CLUNKER OF YOURS.

HOW MUCH DID YOU SAY IT WEIGHS?

BEING A PLACE-KICKER IS LONELY AND NERVE-RACKING.

THERE'S A LOT OF PRESSURE ON US TO MAKE THAT EXTRA POINT.

BUT I'VE MANAGED TO STAY LOOSE AND RELAXED SINCE NOVEMBER 10, 1989.

THAT WAS THE LAST TIME THIS TEAM SCORED A TOUCHDOWN.

By Jeff MacNelly

WHAT SHOULD WE STUFF THE TURKEY WITH THIS YEAR?

I DON'T KNOW...

WHAT DOES UNCLE SID USUALLY EAT?

WHY DO WE ALWAYS EAT THANKSGIVING DINNER SO EARLY?

SO EVERYONE WILL BE GONE LONG BEFORE 'SEINFELD.'

BUT WHY DO WE EAT TURKEY?

IT'S A BIRD, AFTER ALL— LIKE US.

I KNOW.

BUT WE HAVE TO PREPARE THE TURKEY WITH ALL THE FIXINGS.

IT'S AN OLD TRADITION.

AND IT HELPS US TELL THE DIFFERENCE.

WHAT DIFFERENCE?

BETWEEN THE TURKEY ON THE PLATTER...

AND THE TURKEYS AT THE TABLE.

WE BACHELORS BECOME EXPERTS IN SEPARATING OUR LAUNDRY.

THESE ARE THE DIRTY CLOTHES THAT NEED WASHING...

AND THESE ARE THE DIRTY CLOTHES THAT DON'T NEED WASHING YET.

I TOLD YOU: NO SMOKING IN HERE.

I KNOW, I KNOW. THERE'S A STIGMA ATTACHED TO SMOKING CIGARS...

IT'S NOT THAT.

THERE'S ALSO A LOT OF STINKING ATTACHED TO SMOKING CIGARS.

THE HEALTH CARE SYSTEM IS STRANGLED BY PAPERWORK AND BUREAUCRACY.

SO IT'S TIME TO GET THE FEDERAL GOVERNMENT TO STEP IN AND HELP OUT.

ISN'T THAT A LOT LIKE HIRING DR. KEVORKIAN TO BE YOUR PERSONAL TRAINER?

By Jeff MacNelly

SKYLER! GET IN THERE!

COULD I GET A SECOND OPINION?

FOOTBALL IS A LOT LIKE LIFE, I GUESS.

A LOT OF TALK... BIG PLANS...

RED RIGHT, X-9, GREEN, BELLY ONE ON TWO.

A LITTLE YELLING...

HUT ONE HUT TWO HUT! HUT!

SHORT BURSTS OF INTENSE ENERGY...

SMALL PROGRESS...

AND SOME SETBACKS...

FOLLOWED BY EXTENSIVE LEGAL ARGUMENTS.

I LOVE EDITING YOUR COLUMN.

YOU DO?

YUP. THERE'S AN ITALIAN WORD THAT PERFECTLY DESCRIBES THE PROCESS:

CONFETTI.

I'M NOT GOING TO STAND IDLY BY AND WATCH THIS IMPORTANT PIECE OF LEGISLATION GO DOWN TO DEFEAT!

THANK YOU.

I WILL, HOWEVER, SIT IDLY BY...

ABOUT OUR OVERSEAS MILITARY COMMITMENTS...

WE IN CONGRESS THINK THIS IS NO TIME TO CUT AND RUN.

I GUESS IT'S TIME TO TRIM AND DANCE.

I'VE FINISHED CORRECTING YOUR TEST PAPERS...

AND, SKYLER, YOU DID VERY POORLY.

I KNOW. I DON'T TEST VERY WELL.

YOU DON'T HOMEWORK VERY WELL, EITHER.

WHAT HAPPENED TO YOUR GRADES?

MY TEACHER SAYS I AM MANIFESTING A SEVERE ATTENTION DISORDER DUE TO AN OVEREMPHASIS ON COVERT INTERPERSONAL COMMUNICATIVE SKILLS.

TALKING IN CLASS AGAIN?

I'LL HAVE THE VEGGIE BURGER, I GUESS...

OKAY.

AND HOW WOULD YOU LIKE THAT COOKED?

FRIED IN BACON FAT FOR ABOUT TWO DAYS.